A Child's Treasury
of Best-Loved
POEMS

This book is a gift for

_____

from

_____

A Child's Treasury of Best-Loved POEMS

Illustrated by Teddy Edinjiklian

This book is dedicated to my late parents, Agavni and Abraham Edinjiklian. I will cherish their memories as long as I live. – T.E.

ISBN 978-1-60261-220-4

Book design by Miles Parsons
Cover illustration by Ernie Eldredge

Printed in China

Table of Contents

Ladybird

Ladybird! Ladybird! fly away home;
The field mouse is gone to her nest,
The daisies have shut up their sleepy red eyes,
And the birds and the bees are at rest.
Ladybird! Ladybird! fly away home;
The glowworm is lighting her lamp,
The dew's falling fast, and her fine speckled wings
Will flag with the close-clinging damp.
Ladybird! Ladybird! fly away home;
To your house in the old hollow tree,
Where your children so dear have invited the ant
And a few cozy neighbors to tea.
Ladybird! Ladybird! fly away home;
The fairy bells tinkle afar;
Make haste, or they'll catch you and harness you fast
With a cobweb of Oberon's car.
Ladybird! Ladybird! fly away home;
Good luck if you reach it at last!
The owl's come abroad, and the bat's on the roam,
Sharp-set from their diurnal fast.

–*Traditional*

Beautiful Soup

Beautiful Soup, so rich and green,
Waiting in a hot tureen!
Who for such dainties would not stoop?
Soup of the evening, Beautiful Soup!
Soup of the evening, Beautiful Soup!

Beau–ootiful Soo–oop!
Beau–ootiful Soo–oop!
Soo–oop of the e–e–evening,
Beautiful, Beautiful Soup!

Beautiful Soup! Who cares for fish,
Game, or any other dish?
Who would not give all else for two
Pennyworth only of Beautiful Soup?
Pennyworth only of Beautiful Soup?

Beau–ootiful Soo–oop!
Beau–ootiful Soo–oop!
Soo–oop of the e–e–evening,
Beautiful, Beauti–FUL SOUP!

–Lewis Carroll

Three Little Kittens

Three little kittens lost their mittens;
And they began to cry,
O mother dear,
We very much fear
That we have lost our mittens.
Lost your mittens!
You naughty kittens!
Then you shall have no pie.
Mee-ow, mee-ow, mee-ow.
No, you shall have no pie.
Mee-ow, mee-ow, mee-ow.
The three little kittens found their mittens,
And they began to cry,
O mother dear,
See here, see here;
See, we have found our mittens.
Put on your mittens,
You silly kittens,
And you may have some pie.
Purr-r, purr-r, purr-r,
O let us have the pie.
Purr-r, purr-r, purr-r.
The three little kittens put on their mittens,
And soon ate up the pie;
O mother dear,
We greatly fear
That we have soiled our mittens.
Soiled your mittens!
You naughty kittens!
Then they began sigh,
Mee-ow, mee-ow, mee-ow,
Then they began to sigh.
Mee-ow, mee-ow, mee-ow.
The three little kittens washed their mittens,

6

And hung them up to dry;
O mother dear,
Do you hear,
Washed your mittens!
O, you're good kittens.
But I smell a rat close by;
Hush! hush! mee-ow, mee-ow,
We smell a rat close by,
Mee-ow, mee-ow, mee-ow.

–Eliza Lee Follen

7

There Was a Little Girl

There was a little girl
Who had a little curl
Right in the middle of the forehead.
When she was good
She was very, very good,
But when she was bad she was horrid.

–Henry Wadsworth Longfellow

8

The Purple Cow

I never saw a Purple Cow,
I never hope to see one,
But I can tell you, anyhow,
I'd rather see than be one!

–Gelett Burgess

The Circus-Day Parade

Oh the Circus-Day parade! How the Bugles played and played!
And how the glossy horses tossed their flossy manes, and neighed,
As the rattle and rhyme of the tenor-drummer's time
Filled all the hungry hearts of us with melody sublime!
How the grand band-wagon shone with a splendor all its own,
And glittered with a glory that our dreams had never known!
And how the boys behind, high and low of every kind,
Marched in unconscious capture, with a rapture undefined!
How the horsemen, two and two, with their plumes of white and blue,
And crimson, gold and purple, nodding by at me and you,
Waved the banners that they bore, as the Knights in days of yore,
Till our glad eyes gleamed and glistened like the spangles that they wore!
How the graceless-graceful stride of the elephant was eyed,
And the capers of the little horse that cantered at his side!
How the shambling camels, tame to the plaudits of their fame,
With listless eyes came silent, masticating as they came.
How the cages jolted past, with each wagon battened fast,
And the mystery within it only hinted of at last
From the little grated square in the rear, and nosing there
The snout of some strange animal that sniffed the outer air!
And last of all, The Clown, making mirth for all the town,
With lips curved ever upward and his eyebrows down,
And his chief attention paid to the little mule that played
A tattoo on the dashboard with his heels, in the parade.
Oh the Circus-Day parade! How the Bugles played and played!
And how the glossy horses tossed their flossy manes, and neighed,
As the rattle and rhyme of the tenor-drummer's time
Filled all the hungry hearts of us with melody sublime!

–*James Whitcomb Riley*

The Flowerphone

See the morning-glories hung
On the vine for me to use:
Hark! The flower-bell has rung,
I can talk now, if I choose.

Hello Central! Oh, hello!
Give me Puck of Fairy Land –
Mr. Puck, I want to know
What I cannot understand:

How the leaves are scalloped out;
Where's the den of Dragon Fly?
What do Crickets chirp about?
Where do flowers go when they die?

How far can a Fairy see?
Why are woodsy things afraid?
Who lives in the hollow tree?
How are cobweb-carpets made?
Why do Fairies hide? – Hello!
What? I cannot understand –
That's the way they always do,
They've cut me off from Fairy Land!

–*Traditional*

Winter Nights

Blow, wind, blow!
Drift the flying snow!
Send it twirling, whirling overhead!
There's a bedroom in a tree,
Where, snug as snug can be,
The squirrel nests in his cozy bed.
Shriek, wind, shriek!
Make the branches creak!
Battle with the boughs till break o' day!
In a snow cave warm and tight,
Through the icy winter night,
The rabbit sleeps the peaceful hours away.
Call, wind, call,
In entry and in hall,
Straight from off the mountain white and wild!
Soft purrs the cat
On her fluffy mat,
And beside her nestles close her furry child.
Scold, wind, scold,
So bitter and so bold!
Shake the windows with your tap, tap, tap!
With half-shut, dreamy eyes
The drowsy baby lies,
Cuddled close in his mother's lap.

–Mary F. Butts

13

Books

I love my books
They are the homes
Of queens and fairies,
Knights and gnomes.

Each time I read I make a call
On some quaint person large or small,
Who welcomes me with hearty hand
And leads me through his wonderland.

Each book is like
A city street
Along whose winding
Way I meet
New friends and old who laugh and sing
And take me off adventuring!

–*Traditional*

Simple Simon

Simple Simon met a pieman,
Going to the fair;
Says Simple Simon to the pieman,
"Let me taste your ware."
Says the pieman to Simple Simon,
"Show me first your penny."
Says Simple Simon to the pieman,
"Indeed I have not any."
Simple Simon went a-fishing
For to catch a whale;
But all the water he could find
Was in his mother's pail!

–Traditional

Looking Glass River

Smooth it slides upon its travel,
Here a wimple, there a gleam –
    O the clean gravel!
    O the smooth stream!
Sailing blossoms, silver fishes,
Paven pools as clear as air –
    How the child wishes
    To live down there!
We can see our colored faces
Floating on the shaken pool
    Down in cool places
    Dim and very cool;
Till a wind or water wrinkle,
Dipping marten, plumping trout,
    Spreads in a twinkle
    And blots all out.
See the rings pursue each other;
All below grows black as night,
    Just as if mother
    Had blown out the light!
Patience children, just a minute –
See the spreading circles die;
    The stream and all in it
    Will clear by-and-by.

–Robert Louis Stevenson

Little Boy Blue

The little toy dog is covered with dust,
But sturdy and staunch he stands;
The little toy soldier is red with rust,
And his musket moulds in his hands.
Time was when the little toy dog was new,
And the soldier was passing fair;
And that was the time when our Little
    Boy Blue
Kissed them and put them there.

"Now don't you go till I come," he said,
"And don't you make any noise!"
So, toddling off to his trundle bed,
He dreamt of the pretty toys;
And, as he was dreaming, an angel song
Awakened our Little Boy Blue—
Oh! The years are many, the years are long,
But the little toy friends are true!

Aye, faithful to Little Boy Blue they stand,
Each in the same old place,
Awaiting the touch of a little hand,
The smile of a little face;
And they wonder, as waiting the long years
    through
In the dust of that little chair,
What has become of our Little Boy Blue,
Since he kissed them and put them there.

–Eugene Fields

The Cow

The friendly cow all red and white,
I love with all my heart:
She gives me cream with all her might,
To go with apple-tart.

She wanders lowing here and there,
And yet she cannot stray,
All in the pleasant open air,
The pleasant light of day.

And blown by all the winds that pass
And wet with all the showers,
She walks among the meadow grass
And eats the meadow flowers.

–*Robert Louis Stevenson*

Good Night and Good Morning

A fair little girl sat under a tree,
Sewing as long as her eyes could see;
Then smoothed her work and folded it right,
And said, "Dear work, good night, good night!"
Such a number of rooks came over her head,
Crying, "Caw, caw!" on their way to bed.
She said, as she watched their curious flight,
"Little black things, good night, good night, good night!"
The horses neighed, and the oxen lowed,
The sheep's "bleat, bleat!" came over the road;
All seeming to say, with a quiet delight,
"Good little girl, good night, good night!"
She did not say to the sun, "Good night!"
Though she saw him there like a ball of light,
For she knew he had God's time to keep
All over the world, and never could sleep.
The tall pink foxglove bowed his head;
The violets curtsied and went to bed;
And good little Lucy tied up her hair,
And said on her knees her favorite prayer.
And while on her pillow she softly lay,
She knew nothing more till again it was day;
And all things said to the beautiful sun,
"Good morning, good morning! our work is begun."

–Lord Houghton

Twinkle Twinkle Little Star

Twinkle, twinkle, little star;
How I wonder what you are!
Up above the world so high,
Like a diamond in the sky.

When the glorious sun is set,
When the grass with dew is wet,
Then you show your little light,
Twinkle, twinkle, all the night.

When the blazing sun is gone,
When he nothing shines upon,
Then you show your little light,
Twinkle, twinkle, all the night.

In the dark-blue sky you keep,
And often through my curtains peep;
For you never shut your eye
Till the sun is in the sky.

As your bright and tiny spark
Lights the traveler in the dark,
Though I know not what you are,
Twinkle, twinkle, little star.

–Traditional

Mary's Lamb

Mary had a little lamb,
   Its fleece was white as snow;
And everywhere that Mary went,
   The lamb was sure to go.

He followed her to school one day–
   That was against the rule;
It made the children laugh and play,
   To see a lamb at school.

So the teacher turned him out,
   But still he lingered near,
And waited patiently about,
   Till Mary did appear.

Then he ran to her, and laid
   His head upon her arm,
As if he said, "I'm not afraid–
   You'll keep me from all harm."

"What makes the lamb love Mary so?"
   The eager children cry.
"Oh, Mary loves the lamb, you know,"
   The teacher did reply.

–*Sarah Josepha Hale*

Barnyard Song

Won't you come into the barnyard
Where the animals are staying?
Can't you hear the moo-cow mooing
And the hungry horses neighing,
And the baby kittens purring
As they go about their playing?
Oh, it isn't hard to understand
What the animals are saying!
Won't you come into the barnyard
Where the cock is up and crowing,
Where the horse is being harnessed

24

For the plowing and the sowing,
Where the duck has started walking
On his short and waddly legs
To the millpond; and the biddies
All are busy laying eggs,
Where the pigs are taking dust baths
And the pigeons start their cooing?
Oh, it's fun to go and see what
All the animals are doing!

– Traditional

Precocious Piggy

Where are you going to, you little pig?
"I'm leaving my mother, I'm growing so big!"
So big, you young pig.
So young, so big!
What! leaving your mother, you foolish young pig?
Where are you going to, you little pig?
"I've got a new spade, and I'm going to dig!"
To dig, little pig!
A little pig dig!
Well, I never saw a pig with a spade, that could dig!
Where are you going to, you little pig?
"Why I'm going to have a nice ride in a gig!"
In a gig, little pig!
What! a pig in a gig!
Well, I never yet saw a pig ride in a gig!
Where are you going, you little pig?
"I'm going to the barber's to buy me a wig."
A wig, little pig!
A pig in a wig!
Why, whoever before saw a pig in a wig?
Where are you going, you little pig?
"I'm going to the ball to dance a fine jig!"
A jig, little pig!
A pig dance a jig!
Well, I never before saw a pig dance a jig!

–Thomas Hodd

26

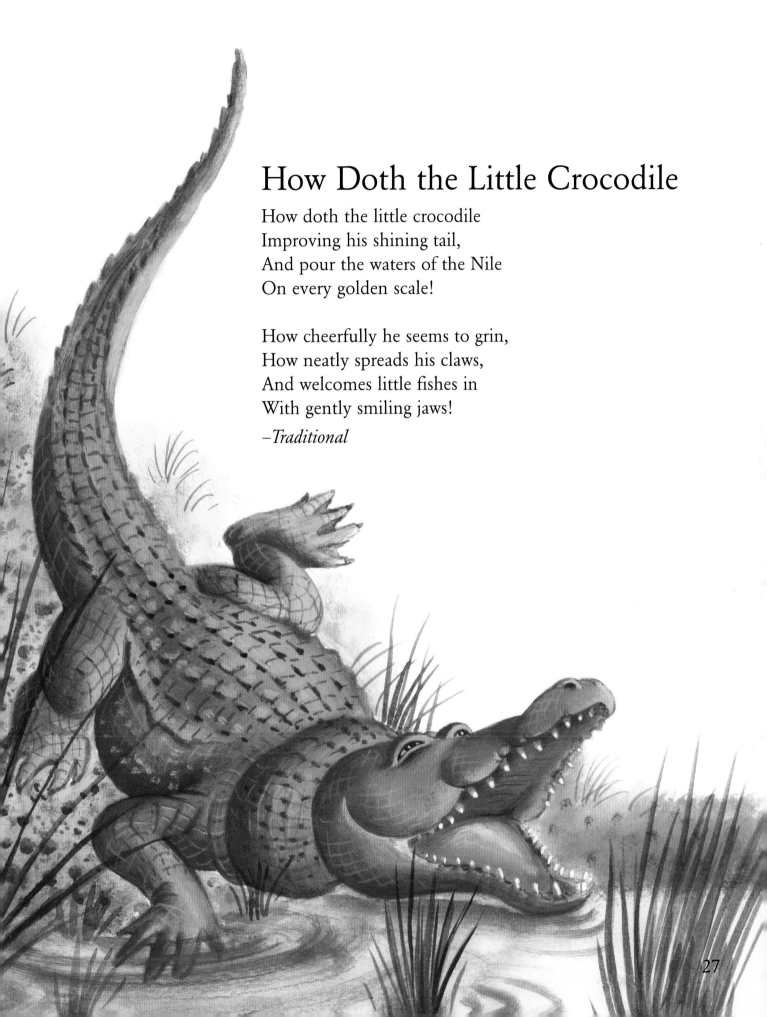

How Doth the Little Crocodile

How doth the little crocodile
Improving his shining tail,
And pour the waters of the Nile
On every golden scale!

How cheerfully he seems to grin,
How neatly spreads his claws,
And welcomes little fishes in
With gently smiling jaws!

–*Traditional*

The Sugar-Plum Tree

Have you ever heard of the Sugar-Plum
   Tree?
'Tis a marvel of great renown!
It blooms on the shore of Lollipop sea,
In the garden of Shut-Eye Town.

The fruit it bears is wondrously sweet
(As those who have tasted it say)
That good little children have only to eat
Of that fruit to be happy next day.

When you've got to the tree, you would
   have a hard time
To capture the fruit of which I sing;
The tree is so tall no person could climb
To the boughs where the sugar-plums swing!

But up in the tree sits a chocolate cat,
And a gingerbread dog prowls below.
And this is the way you contrive to get at
Those sugar-plums tempting you so.

You say but the word to the gingerbread
  dog
And he barks with such terrible zest
That the chocolate cat is at one all agog,
As her swelling proportions attest.
And the chocolate cat goes cavorting
  around
From this leafy limb unto that,
And the sugar-plums tumble, of course to
  the ground
Hooray for the chocolate cat!

There are marshmallows, gumdrops, and
  peppermint canes,
With stripings of silver and gold,
And you carry away of the treasure that
  rains
As much as your apron can hold!

So come, little children, cuddle closer to
  me
In your dainty white night cap and gown,
And I'll rock you away to that Sugar-Plum
  Tree
In the garden of Shut-Eye Town.

–Eugene Fields

Wynken, Blynken, and Nod

Wynken, Blynken, and Nod one night
Sailed off in a wooden shoe—
Sailed on a river of crystal light,
Into a sea of dew.
"Where are you going, and what do you
    wish?"
The old moon asked the three.
"We have come to fish for the herring fish
That live in this beautiful sea;
Nets of silver and gold have we!"
Said Wynken,
Blynken,
And Nod.

The old moon laughed and sang a song,
As they rocked in the wooden shoe,
And the wind that sped them all night long
Ruffled the waves of dew.
The little stars were the herring fish
That lived in that beautiful sea—
"Now cast your nets wherever you wish—
Never afeard are we";
So cried the stars to the fishermen three:
Wynken,
Blynken,
And Nod.

All night long their nets they threw
To the stars in the twinkling foam—
Then down from the skies came the
    wooden shoe,
Bringing the fishermen home;
'Twas all so pretty a sail it seemed
As if it could not be,
And some folks thought 'twas a dream
    they'd dreamed
Of sailing that beautiful sea—
Now I shall name you the fishermen three:
Wynken,
Blynken,
And Nod.

Wynken and Blynken are two little eyes,
And Nod is a little head,
And the wooden shoe that sailed the skies
Is the wee one's trundle-bed.
So shut your eyes while mother sings
Of wonderful sights that be,
And you shall see the beautiful things
As you rock in the misty sea,
Where the old shoe rocked the fishermen
    three:
Wynken,
Blynken,
And Nod.

–*Eugene Fields*

31

My Shadow

I have a little shadow that goes in and out with me,
And what can be the use of him is more than I can see.
He is very, very like me from the heels up to the head;
And I see him jump before me when I jump into my bed.
The funniest thing about him is the way he likes to grow,
Not at all like proper children, which is always very slow;
For sometimes he shoots up taller like an Indian rubber ball,
And he sometimes gets so little that there is none of him at all.

He hasn't got a notion of how children ought to play,
And can only make a fool of me in every sort of way.
He stays so close behind me he's a coward you can see;
I'd think shame to stick to nursie as that shadow
sticks to me!

One morning, very early before the sun was up,
I rose and found the shining dew on every
buttercup;
But my lazy little shadow like an arrant sleepy-
head,
Had stayed at home behind me and was fast
asleep in bed.

–Robert Louis Stevenson

32